# ALL ABOUT BEARS
## An A to Z of Bears

For Diana

Written by Brian Miles.
Illustrated by Pam Storey.

Published by Grandreams Limited
435-437 Edgware Road, Little Venice, London, W2 1TH.

 is for **A**irman Bear
Who takes off in his plane,
He flies around in circles
Then he lands again.

# Bb

is for **B**us Driver Bear
Driving through the town,
He stops to pick the bears up
Then he sets them down.

C c is for the **C**owboy Bear
    Riding the range on his horse,
    He loves to sit around the fire
    And eat baked beans of course!

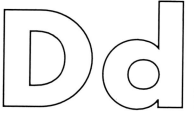

**Dd** is for the **D**iver Bear
Exploring an ancient wreck,
He's hoping to find some treasure
Hidden below the deck.

**Ee** is for **E**ngine Driver Bear
Almost ready to go,
He's about to pull the lever
To make the whistle blow.

# Ff

is for brave **F**ireman Bear
Swaying to and fro,
Hosing water from his ladder
On the fire below.

# Gg

is for **G**ood Old Bear
Sleeping in his rocking chair,
Listening to the birds and bees
He doesn't have a care.

 is for **H**ungry Bear
Eating lots of bread and honey,
He's made a picnic in the woods
Where it's warm and sunny.

Ii is for Indian Bear
One who is very brave,
He already has a wigwam
But likes to live in a cave.

# Jj

is for **J**oker Bear
He is always playing tricks,
He can take real chicken eggs
And turn them into chicks!

# Kk

is for the **K**ing Bear
Sitting upright on the throne,
Should you wish to talk to him
Just call him on the phone.

# Ll

is for **L**ittle **L**onely Bear
As lonely as can be,
He wonders why he's so lonely
He only has one flea!

# Mm

is for the **M**usic Bear
Singing and playing the drums,
He can't remember all the words
So now and then he hums!

# Nn

is for old **N**osey Bear
With his very long nose,
You can't keep secrets from Nosey
Because he always knows!

is for **O**utrageous Bear
He just doesn't have a care,
Dressed in bright pink trousers
He'll wear anything for a dare!

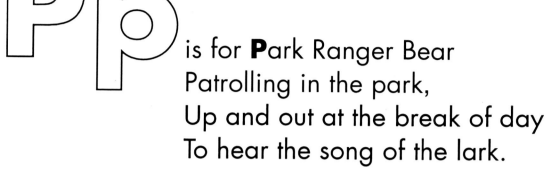

# Pp

is for **P**ark Ranger Bear
Patrolling in the park,
Up and out at the break of day
To hear the song of the lark.

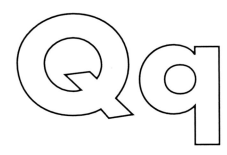

**Qq** is for **Q**uickly Bear
Darting along the trail,
He's hoping to meet Post Bear
With the morning mail.

# Rr

Now **R** is for **R**otund Bear
Which means, well, he's rather fat,
After eating lots of honey
He gives his tum a pat!

# Ss

is for old **S**leepy Bear
He is such a sleepy head,
He's up so late in the day
That it's time to go to bed!

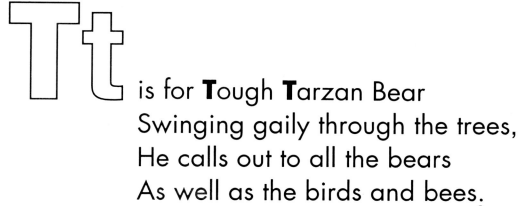

# Tt

is for **T**ough **T**arzan Bear
Swinging gaily through the trees,
He calls out to all the bears
As well as the birds and bees.

# Uu is for nice **U**ncle Bear
A cheerful chap is he,
He always brings a lovely cake
When he comes to tea.

# Vv

is for **V**ery Good Bear
And a very good bear is he,
He always says "Please" and "Thank you"
And is never late for tea.

# Ww

is for **W**restler Bear
He enjoys a good old scrap,
He loves a rough and tumble
But he's really a friendly chap.

# Xx

Now **X** is for E**X**tra Bear
Who's extra, extra good,
He'll bake a cake and make some tea
He's really very good.

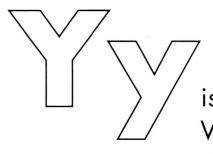

**Y**y is for **Y**ummy Bear
Who always says "Yum! Yum!"
Especially when there's food about
For his little tum!

# Zz

is for **Z**izzy Bear
Who snores so loud each night,
Zzz, zzz and zzz he snores
He's really quite a sight.

# Teddy Goes To School

"I'm glad to be going to school today,"
Said Teddy, hearing the bell,
"I am going to learn to read and write
And add and subtract as well."

"I want to know where Australia is
And where do bananas grow,
I want to know what the Inuit eat
And why they have all that snow."

"I want to know where the rivers begin
And what makes the oceans swell,
And how does the salt get into the sea
I know the teachers will tell."

"I want to know all about this big world
And why it's round like a ball,
And I want to know all about giraffes
And what makes their necks so tall."